GCSE PERFORMANCE PIECES
CLARINET

SERIES EDITOR: ANDREW S. COXON
COMPILED BY: HOWARD McGILL

RHINEGOLD
EDUCATION

Other titles in this series:
Flute, Alto Saxophone, Guitar, Bass Guitar, Drums, Piano, Voice

Rhinegold Education also publishes GCSE and A Level Study Guides, Listening Tests and Revision Guides for the Edexcel, AQA and OCR specifications.

First published 2012 in Great Britain by Rhinegold Education, 14–15 Berners Street, London W1T 3LJ
www.rhinegoldeducation.co.uk

© 2012 Rhinegold Education
a division of Music Sales Limited

GCSE Performance Pieces: Clarinet
Order No. RHG536
ISBN: 978-1-78038-638-6
Exclusive Distributors:
Music Sales Ltd
Distribution Centre, Newmarket Road
Bury St Edmunds, Suffolk IP33 3YB, UK

Edited by Ruth Power
CD mixed and mastered by Jonas Persson

Printed in the EU

Design by www.penguinboy.net
Images courtesy of Getty Images.

ABOUT THE SERIES EDITOR

Andrew Coxon graduated from York University with a joint Honours Degree in Music and English before going on to Leeds University to complete a PGCE, and later gained a further degree through the Open University. He has had a teaching career spanning more than 40 years, for the most part as a Head of Department, and has been an examiner and moderator for many years, currently holding a senior GCSE examining position. He has recently authored music education materials for Rhinegold Education and Nelson Thornes.

Having spent most of his professional life in the North East, he now teaches part-time in Cumbria where he lives with his wife, son and a border collie. He still gains tremendous enjoyment from his classroom work, organising two instrumental groups and taking part in regular concerts, all in addition to his regular church organ-playing duties.

ABOUT THE AUTHOR

Howard McGill is a prolific session musician of a range of instruments including soprano, alto, tenor and baritone saxophones; clarinet and bass clarinet; flute, alto flute and piccolo; wind synth and percussion.

In his youth, Howard received multiple awards and scholarships for his jazz playing, performing with the BBC Big Band, and the National Youth Jazz Orchestra. At 21 he won the BBC Don Lusher Prize for Best Up and Coming Jazz Musician in Britain. After graduating with honours in engineering, Howard studied jazz and studio music at the Guildhall School of Music and Drama. He played in numerous West End Shows, and has played alongside a host of legendary performers including Frank Sinatra, Donna Summer and Shirley Bassey. Howard has also worked in the pop scene, touring extensively with Vanessa Mae, playing opposite Michael Jackson, the Spice Girls and Ben Folds 5 as well as performing for the Queen.

Howard opened Station House Studios in 1998 and was signed to Artemis Music as a media composer. He produced the Go Solo improvisation series, the Associated Board Jazz Works, Take the Lead and Jazztastic series published by IMP.

ACKNOWLEDGEMENTS

The publisher wishes to thank the copyright holders, without whose kind permission this book would not have been possible, and Sam Corkin for his assistance.

INTRODUCTION

This book offers ten pieces for you to play. They are at a range of standards, from the equivalent of Grade 3 through to Grade 6, in order of increasing difficulty. However, as these pieces have not been set by any examination board thus far, grades are given as guides and you should ask your teacher to check with the GCSE examination board and/or its specification for a final ruling.

The book contains a mixture of popular songs, some of which will be very familiar to you and others which may not, but I am sure you will gain great satisfaction from being able to play them well. They each present different demands, from the legato phrasing on the hauntingly beautiful 'Memory' to the strong sense of rhythm and clear, precise articulation on 'Grenade' and the wide range of dynamics on 'Viva la Vida'.

The important thing to do when thinking about what to prepare for a performance examination is to choose something which is comfortably within your technical abilities. It is not a good idea to choose a piece on the basis that it is hard and will therefore gain you a higher mark for difficulty. More marks may be available for harder pieces but with any examination board at GCSE it is your ability to play the notes and rhythms correctly, to show that you understand the style and character of the piece, and to demonstrate that you can play it with total confidence and conviction that will gain you most marks. You are, after all, giving a musical performance and you would not want to go to a concert to hear very difficult pieces played badly!

With each piece, there is expert advice on how to approach it, what you should look out for (for example, particular techniques you need to master) and how to shape the piece into a really musical performance. Please read this through carefully before you start on any of the pieces and be prepared to refer back to it if you need to.

I am sure you will find plenty of music in this book to enjoy and will have great success playing the wide range of tunes.

Good luck!

Andrew Coxon
Series Editor

SUGGESTED LISTENING

A YouTube playlist has been created containing all the songs in this book for you to listen to. The playlist also contains any additional suggested listening the author recommends, including cover versions and wider listening to help you get a feel for each song and its cultural context. Listening to a wide range of music will help you create your own interpretation.

Access the playlist by searching YouTube for 'Rhinegold Education', where you'll find our channel and the playlist within it. Alternatively, scan this QR code with your smartphone to go straight there.

BRING HIM HOME

LES MISÉRABLES

GRADE 3 STANDARD

A performer from Les Misérables

Les Misérables is one of the most famous musicals of all time. Based on the novel by Victor Hugo follows the struggles of a cast of characters as they seek redemption and revolution in 19th century France. French composer Claude–Michel Schönberg composed the score in 1980, with a libretto by Alain Boublil. It was first staged in London's West End in 1985, with English lyrics by Herbert Kretzmer, and in 2010 it celebrated its 25th anniversary, becoming the longest–running West End musical in history.

This is a beautiful song full of emotion. The key to playing it well is to achieve a warm and focused sound by using just the right amount of pressure on the mouthpiece. If your reed is too soft your sound will be too thin for this piece. Really shape the end of each phrase so that the note doesn't end too abruptly. Give the triplet in bar 11 plenty of time. The entire song requires very smooth legato playing: take care that there are no glitches between notes by concentrating on your breath control.

SONG STATS

Tempo: Slow ♩=69

Key: C major

Range:

The chorus at bar 26 should build nicely through the upper register without sounding at all shrill. Have a round tone at all times. This applies to the *Dal Segno (D.S al Coda)*, when the melody is up an octave: try to keep control of the tone just as you did in the lower register the first time round.

You should take care to breathe correctly so that the sound is supported and doesn't begin to quiver. Practise creating a pure, focused tone with no reed noise.

SUGGESTED LISTENING

Listen to the performance by renowned singer Alfie Boe to really get a feel for the emotion of the song.

BRING HIM HOME

Music by Claude–Michel Schönberg
Lyrics by Alain Boublil & Herbert Kretzmer
© Copyright 1985 (Music & Lyrics) Alain Boublil Music Limited.
All Rights Reserved. International Copyright Secured.

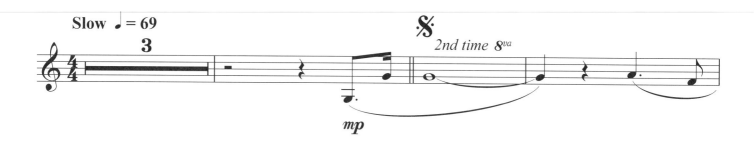

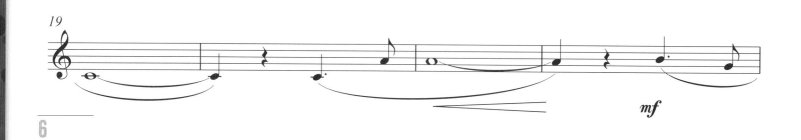

to Coda ⊕

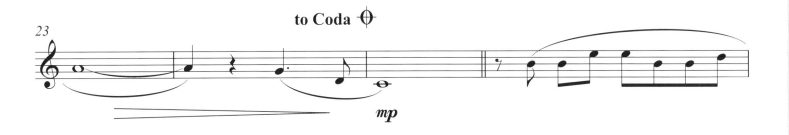

mp

mf

D.S. al Coda

p   *mp*

⊕ Coda

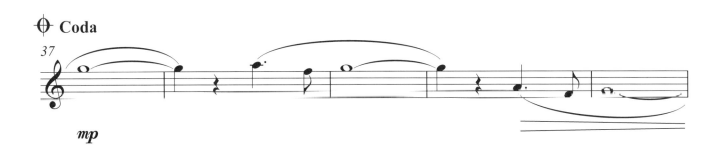

mp

p   *pp*

7

FORGET YOU
CEE LO GREEN
GRADE 3 STANDARD

Cee Lo Green

Cee Lo Green released 'Forget You' in 2010 as the first single from his third studio album, *The Lady Killer*. The song has flavours of soul and Motown with the baritone sax riff throughout, played in this version in the pianist's left hand.

The key to this song is playing rhythmically, locking into the groove and also playing with attitude – this is not a time to play in a soft and subtle manner but to really dig into those rhythms. Don't over blow though!

Really listen carefully to the backing track to place the phrases just so. Be careful to follow the cue notes at the start: it is easy to hear the opening across the bar, for example, beat 1 doesn't sound like beat 1!

Try to imagine singing the words as you play to get the right articulation, for example, bar 5 should be played with legato quavers and crotchets.

SONG STATS

Performance directions: Energetically and rhythmically

Tempo: ♩=127

Range:

SUGGESTED LISTENING

Listen to the way Cee Lo Green places the phrases in the song and gives the whole piece character.

There is a really funky rhythm in bar 12 which is particularly syncopated. Make sure you place this correctly. This runs straight into the middle section of the verse at the end of the bar, so try to make sense of this melody line.

Bars 15 and 16 have some nice staccato figures which you should try to keep detached. The bridge section at bar 21 should have a less legato feel and be more punchy.

The end of the chorus from bar 28 should sing out as it rises into the upper register with very rhythmic and detached playing in bars 31 and 32.

FORGET YOU

CAN'T HELP FALLING IN LOVE
ELVIS PRESLEY
GRADE 3 STANDARD

Elvis Presley

'Can't Help Falling in Love' was originally recorded by Elvis Presley. It featured in his 1961 film, *Blue Hawaii*, and topped the British charts in 1962. It has been covered by numerous artists over the years, including British reggae group UB40, whose 1993 version topped the US and UK charts, and Swedish pop group A*Teens, whose version featured in the soundtrack of Disney's *Lilo and Stitch*.

The version in this book is in $\frac{12}{8}$ time signature, meaning literally 12 quavers or eighth notes per bar. These 12 beats are felt as four groups of three, giving a triplet feel to the pulse. Care should be taken when the notes go against this triplet feel, for example at the end of bar 8 where the last half of the bar is written as three crotchets. The phrase still needs to flow smoothly even with these cross rhythms.

SONG STATS

Performance directions:
Slow 50s style

Tempo: ♩. =68

Range:

To play this piece well involves the mastery of long smooth phrases with good breath control. Each four-bar phrase should be played in one breath. Although the opening verse is fairly soft (***mp***), make sure the sound remains focused, using enough pressure on the mouthpiece and reed. Very little tongue should be used in these opening phrases, just start the first note with a gentle articulation and then slur the following notes smoothly together with good finger coordination.

The second statement of the verse from bar 11, although a straight repeat of the melody, should have a little more intensity to the sound in order to build towards the chorus at bar 19. Be sure to play nice and smoothly across the break in bars 19–21 into the chorus.

The chorus should be a little louder and intensify as the line rises up into the second register in two bar phrases. Again, the melody written in crotchets cuts across the triplet feel for the first three bars. This is unusual in being a five-bar phrase. Try to give it shape both within each bar and also over the five-bar phrase.

For a more difficult version, bar 32 to the end could be played up an octave, still with the same focus of sound and melody contours. If you decide to do this, be sure to make your intentions clear for an examination performance.

SUGGESTED LISTENING

Compare Elvis's original recording with the range of cover versions to give you ideas for your own interpretation.

CAN'T HELP FALLING IN LOVE

Words & Music by George David Weiss, Hugo Peretti & Luigi Creatore
© Copyright 1961 Gladys Music.

In a slow 50s style ♩= 68

mp molto legato e espr.

GRENADE
BRUNO MARS
GRADE 4 STANDARD

Bruno Mars

'Grenade' was released in 2010 by American singer/songwriter and producer Bruno Mars, and was the second single from his debut studio album *Doo-Wops & Hooligans*. It was co-written by Mars along with his production team The Smeezingtons with Brody Brown, Claude Kelly and Andrew Wyatt.

This version for clarinet requires a good sense of rhythm and solid articulation. Everything should be tongued in a rhythmic fashion to create a groove to the melodic line. This, however, should not sound too staccato; more of a legato tongue should be used to connect the notes together, for example bars 11–14.

SONG STATS

Performance directions: Expressively

Tempo: ♩=111

Range:

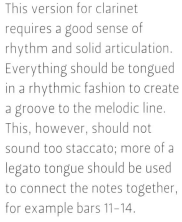

There are varying degrees of articulation, from full legato phrases to legato tongue to odd staccato notes. Care should be taken to point out all these differences in articulation without detracting from the melody.

The song should start off softly and crescendo towards the climax. Try to lock into the rhythmic groove. The lyrics of the chorus describe the pain of unrequited love – try to capture something of the intensity of that feeling in your performance.

SUGGESTED LISTENING

Watch the promotional video to see the story played out as you listen to the lyrics – this will give you a feel for the emotion you need to convey.

GRENADE

Expressively ♩ = 111

(hi-hat cue)

mp

mf

f

HALLELUJAH
LEONARD COHEN
GRADE 4 STANDARD

Leonard Cohen

Written by Canadian singer/songwriter Leonard Cohen, 'Hallelujah' was originally released on his studio album *Various Positions* in 1984. The song has been featured significantly in film and television soundtracks, was famously covered by the late Jeff Buckley in 1994, and was given a new lease of life when Alexandra Burke sang it to win *The X-Factor* in 2008.

This song is a real test of stamina. Its slow tempo means that you will need to concentrate on breathing properly from the diaphragm to support the long notes. Set in $\frac{12}{8}$ with a triplet feel, the rhythms are particularly challenging and care should be taken to play them exactly as they are written. It may help to slow the tempo right down when practising and mark out the quaver pulse to see exactly where the beats land, and then gradually speed it up.

SONG STATS

Performance directions:
Expressively

Tempo: ♩. =61

Range:

The opening verse should be played with a quiet but centred sound. It is all too easy to play with a soft 'woolly' sub tone sound, but by applying a little more pressure on the mouthpiece and reed you can achieve a more focused effect. The verse should be played in a very legato style with only soft articulation, not too much tongue or reed noise.

Try to give the melody line space, even when the rhythms appear to be quick, for example in bar 4 – make sure this doesn't sound rushed. Similarly, in bar 20 make sure the semiquavers don't sound scrambled. From bar 33, this upper register melody can really sing out with a pure rounded tone. From here on the final chorus should gradually die out with each phrase like an echo of the previous one.

Dynamically, the verse should build gradually up towards the chorus. Keep the sound controlled so that the chorus from bar 11 sings out, capturing the emotion of the song without sounding raucous.

SUGGESTED LISTENING

Listen to the different interpretations of this song by Rufus Wainwright, Alexandra Burke and Jeff Buckley to get a feel for the yearning lyrics and heart-felt emotion.

HALLELUJAH

Words & Music by Leonard Cohen
© Copyright 1984 Sony/ATV Music Publishing.

Expressively ♩. = 61

mp cantabile

cresc. poco a poco

f

mf espressivo

mf cantabile

f

mf espressivo

molto rall.

VIVA LA VIDA
COLDPLAY
GRADE 4 STANDARD

Coldplay (left to right):
Jonny Buckland, Chris Martin, Guy Berryman, Will Champion

'Viva La Vida' from the Coldplay album *Viva La Vida or Death and All His Friends* literally means "long live life". The lyrics contain a lot of strong historical and revolutionary references, which give the piece an anthem-like quality.

'Viva La Vida' starts with an incredibly infectious riff, which repeats throughout the song. This riff is a rhythmic pattern played by strings and drums alternating 'on' beats with 'off' beats (syncopation). The repeated figure has a hypnotic effect and gives a real sense of anticipation to the song, like something big is about to happen.

SONG STATS

Performance directions:
Lightly

Tempo: ♩ =138

Range:

SUGGESTED LISTENING

Listen to the original to hear how the long melody floats over the opening riff, and to get a sense of the building tension.

As you start playing, remember that you need to have somewhere to build to. Start softly then slowly crescendo through the verses to the chorus at bar 41. Think of this as the high point of the song. After the chorus, the phrase at bar 72 can really sing out, especially when it goes up the octave. Don't let the long notes die: keep them alive to the very end of the note value.

As you perform this piece you'll need to demonstrate that you can play both lyrically and rhythmically. Try to keep the melody sustained and connected by a long phrase mark. Pay particular attention to the rhythms in bars 29 to 37 as they can be tricky. For the articulation, use a light tongue in bar 28, and then even tonguing in bar 36. Also use light accents to emphasise points in the rhythm, and use the seven bar-long rests to catch your breath and compose.

You'll also need to lock into the rhythm. This is about feeling the groove and internalising it – move to the music or tap your foot, whatever helps you feel the beat. Count carefully throughout to keep up as it can be very repetitive.

Make this piece your own individual anthem. Don't feel restricted to the notes as they're written on the page. Feel free to change the rhythms as if you yourself were singing the song through your instrument. However, if you do this when you perform the piece for an examination, you must indicate that the score is a guide and you have put your own interpretation upon it. You may find it helpful to play from memory to free yourself up from just reading the notes: let's hear you really express yourself.

VIVA LA VIDA

Words & Music by Guy Berryman, Jon Buckland, Will Champion & Chris Martin

Lightly ♩ = 138

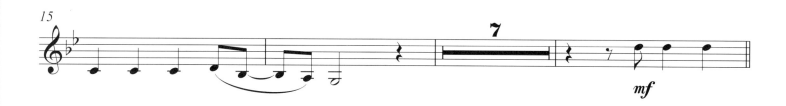

Optional

I SAY A LITTLE PRAYER
ARETHA FRANKLIN
GRADE 5 STANDARD

Aretha Franklin

Aretha Franklin's 1968 single, 'I Say A Little Prayer', was written by Burt Bacharach and Hal David. The original recording in 1967 was sung by Dionne Warwick while Bacharach arranged, conducted and played the piano.

Like several Bacharach compositions, the chorus contains passages written in unusual time signatures. The verses are made up of two successive bars of $\frac{4}{4}$, a bar of $\frac{10}{4}$ (using $\frac{4}{4}$ + $\frac{2}{4}$ + $\frac{4}{4}$), and two final bars of $\frac{4}{4}$. The chorus is in $\frac{11}{4}$ (using $\frac{4}{4}$ + $\frac{3}{4}$ + $\frac{4}{4}$). So remember to count carefully the number of beats in each bar, but allow the melody to flow freely over the top.

Playing this piece well is all about good articulation. There are many repeated notes, for example, in bar 13, which need to be tongued evenly and gently.

The articulation in bars 25, 27 and 28 needs to be paid special attention: at bar 25 the articulation is long, short, long, long, short, long (which is repeated in bar 28). Then for the articulation at bar 27 we have long, long.

This attention to detail will show the examiners that you have studied this piece thoroughly.

FACT BOX
Tempo: Medium fast
Range:

SUGGESTED LISTENING

Check out the iconic Dionne Warwick rendition as well as the Aretha Franklin version to capture a little of the feel of the sixties.

I SAY A LITTLE PRAYER

Words by Hal David
Music by Burt Bacharach
© Copyright 1966 Casa David Music Incorporated/New Hidden Valley Music Company.
Universal/MCA Music Limited/Warner/Chappell Music Publishing Limited.
All Rights Reserved. International Copyright Secured.

Medium fast tempo

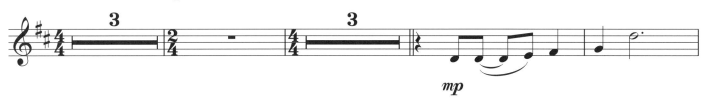

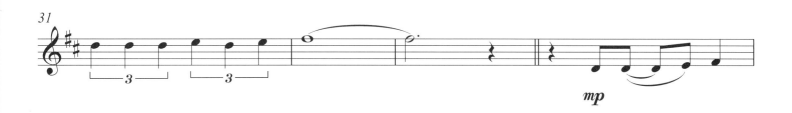

MEMORY

CATS
GRADE 5 STANDARD

Characters from Cats

'Memory', by Andrew Lloyd Webber, is from the musical *Cats*. The song is sung by the character Grizabella, who was once known as the 'Glamour Cat', and is now just a shadow of her former self. The song therefore has a nostalgic flavour as she remembers the good old days. It is sung near the beginning of the musical in brief but reappears near the end as the climax of the whole show. It is by far the most popular and well-known song from *Cats*, and is a beautiful, lyrical piece which suits the clarinet very well.

A key element of this piece is to play a smooth melody with each note connected to the next. For example, bars 10 and 11 should be one phrase with no breaks between notes. This applies to bars 12 and 13 similarly. Keep your breath going constantly so the sound never falters.

SONG STATS

Performance directions:
Freely

Tempo: ♩. =50

Range:

Make sure you play in tune with the flute sound in the backing track the second time through from bar 2. Sing out at bar 26, but be careful not to produce a shrill sound. Keep in mind the climax of the piece at bar 42 — make sure you have enough breath to produce the dynamics and expression needed.

This piece tests the entire range of the clarinet from low to high and the dynamic range from piano (*p*) to fortissimo (*ff*). Make sure the contours of the melody match the dynamic variation, and take care to ensure the tone is balanced across the break (above and below B♮) throughout.

SUGGESTED LISTENING

Listen to the song as performed in the musical *Cats* and hear the sadness and melancholy you need to convey in your rendition.

MEMORY

Music by Andrew Lloyd Webber
Text by Trevor Nunn after T.S. Eliot
Music © Copyright 1981 Andrew Lloyd Webber licensed to The Really Useful Group Limited.
Text © Copyright 1981 Trevor Nunn/Set Copyrights Limited/Faber Music Limited.
All Rights Reserved. International Copyright Secured.

SOMEONE LIKE YOU
ADELE GRADE 5 STANDARD

Adele

Adele wrote this song with American singer/songwriter and producer Dan Wilson for her second studio album *21*. It features Adele's voice accompanied solely by an undulating piano backing. The song is a heart-felt reflection of a relationship that's over. With lyrics like these, every note you play needs to be charged with emotion.

The song should start with an introverted feel, just like you are playing to yourself and no one else. Think about the opening lyrics in Adele's song and how reflective they are: try to express this as you play.

It's a real test in stamina: make sure you breathe properly from the diaphragm and give the melody a pure, focused tone with no reed noise. Take the reed off to dry and reset it just before you play. Count carefully throughout as the piece should be at a steady tempo. Although the rhythms appear fast on the page (bars 15-16) with lots of semiquavers and syncopated rhythms, they should never sound rushed.

SONG STATS

Performance directions: Smoothly, with tenderness

Tempo: ♩=68

Range:

When the chorus starts at bar 22, this is where you want everyone to hear you! The melody needs to hold its head up high with a strong, resolute quality – this should be helped by the fact that you're in the upper register at this point. When it does occasionally drop down to the lower register (below B♮), make sure the tone is good and strong. The transition between upper and lower register should be as smooth as possible so there's no discernible change in colour.

You could experiment with tone colours throughout the development of the song. Try sub-tone at the start of the verse building to full-tone for the chorus. Sub-tone is achieved by using less pressure on the mouthpiece so the tone becomes spread and blends into the background. Full-tone requires more pressure and results in a more focussed and centred sound which stands out more.

SUGGESTED LISTENING

Listen to Adele's recording to get a feel for the raw emotion in the song.

This will help both dynamically and with the emotional communication of your playing. Remember to keep the tempo steady at bar 59 as the backing becomes sparse here. At bar 70 you will need careful intonation to lock in with the piano pitch. Take your time over every note so that each phrase really means something and is not just thrown away.

SOMEONE LIKE YOU

Words & Music by Adele Adkins & Daniel Wilson
© Copyright 2010 Universal Music Publishing Limited/
Sugar Lake Music/Chrysalis Music Limited.
All Rights Reserved. International Copyright Secured.

Smoothly, with tenderness ♩ = 68

mp espressivo

mf

poco cresc.

mp — *p*

poco rit.   a tempo

FLY ME TO THE MOON
FRANK SINATRA
GRADE 6 STANDARD

Frank Sinatra

Composed in 1954, 'Fly Me To The Moon' is perhaps the best known of all swing pieces. Covered by countless artists, it remains a popular choice to this day on TV talent shows across the world.

This is the hardest piece in the book, and is beyond what is required in the GCSE syllabus. Only choose this piece if you are confident that you can deliver it well – a slightly easier piece played well and comfortably will get you more marks than a harder piece played less well.

The examiners will be looking not just for accuracy but also for a really big-band swing feel that captures the toe-tapping spirit of the piece. Aim for a punchy sound, keep quaver stabs such as those in the first few bars short and punchy, and strive for effortless swung quavers throughout.

Given the difficulty of this piece, it is important that you practise some of the sections slowly first – for example at bar 56 onwards. Try using a metronome on these difficult phrases, very gradually increasing the speed over a period of weeks – before you know it you'll be playing it up to tempo! For extra marks, include the grace note in bar 46, and do a fast glissando up to the top D in bar 56. Finally, take great care over the rhythms at bar 64 onwards, ensuring that you come in confidently on the offbeat tied quavers.

SONG STATS

Tempo: Medium Fast

♩ =88

Range:

SUGGESTED LISTENING

Listen to Frank Sinatra's iconic version which was even played by the astronauts of Apollo 11 on the moon itself during the lunar landings of 1969! For a range of different interpretations, try Sarah Vaughan, Doris Day, Diana Krall and the modern take by Rizzle Kicks.

FLY ME TO THE MOON

D.S. al Coda
(with repeat)

✛ *Coda*